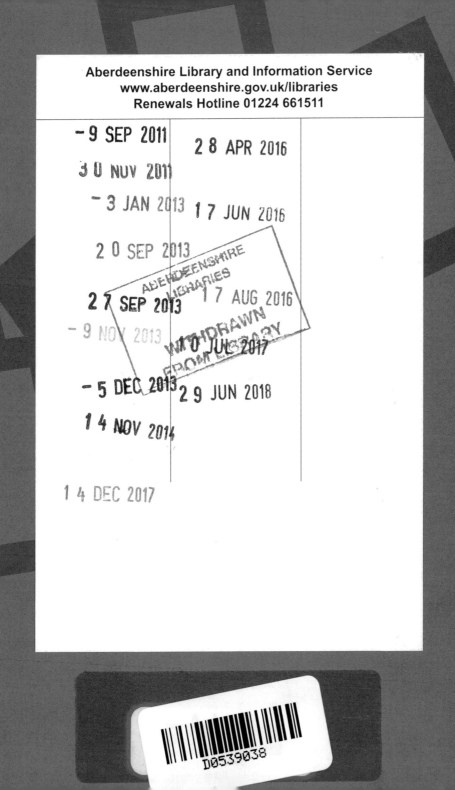

Odysseus

and the
Wooden Horse

First published in 2008 by
Franklin Watts
338 Euston Road
London
NW1 3BH

Franklin Watts Australia
Level 17/207 Kent Street
Sydney
NSW 2000

A CIP catalogue record for this book is available
from the British Library.

ISBN 978 0 7496 7994 1 (hbk)
ISBN 978 0 7496 8002 2 (pbk)

Series Editor: Melanie Palmer
Series Advisor: Dr Barrie Wade
Series Designer: Peter Scoulding

Printed in China

Franklin Watts is a division of
Hachette Children's Books,
an Hachette Livre UK company
www.hachettelivre.co.uk

Odysseus
and the
Wooden Horse

by Damian Harvey and Martin Remphry

FRANKLIN WATTS
LONDON•SYDNEY

Long ago, the Trojans and the
Greeks were at war. The Trojan
king sent his sons, Hector and
Paris, to Greece to make peace.

But in Greece, Paris fell in love with the Greek king's beautiful wife, Helen. He took her back to Troy.

The king of Greece was furious.
He gathered his armies, led by
mighty Odysseus. They sailed
to Troy to bring Helen back.

Outside the walls of Troy there was
a great battle. Each side sent their
best fighters. Odysseus chose the
Greek heroes, Ajax and Achilles.

The Trojans chose their princes,
Hector and Paris. The others
hid behind the huge city walls.

First Ajax swung his huge hammer
at Hector, but he missed. Hector
knocked Ajax down.

Then Hector was hit by the spear of Achilles, the greatest Greek warrior of all.

Next Paris took out his arrow and shot Achilles in the heel. The great Achilles fell down dead.

Odysseus was shocked to see his best soldier killed. "We must get into the city of Troy," he said.

But the Greeks could not break into the city. The walls were too high and the gates were too strong.

Then clever Odysseus had an idea.
"Build me a great wooden horse,"
he ordered. "Make it big enough
for me and my men to fit inside."

For many days and nights the
Greeks worked hard to build a
huge wooden horse.

When it was ready, Odysseus led
his men inside. "Now we will
trick the Trojans," he said.

"Hide the ships nearby," Odysseus told the Greeks. The armies pretended to sail away, leaving only the wooden horse behind.

The Trojans saw the Greeks sailing away. "We've won!" they cheered.

"Look, the Greeks have left us a gift," said the Trojans, looking at the wooden horse. They pushed it right up to the city gates.

20

Odysseus and his men kept
very quiet. If they made a
sound, their plan would fail.

But some of the Trojans were worried. "What if it's a trick?" asked one soldier. He threw his spear at the horse's belly.

Odysseus and his men kept very still. No one dared to move. "No, it's just a gift after all," the Trojans cried.

The Trojans opened the gates and pulled the huge horse into the city.

That night they had a great party
to celebrate the end of the war.

25

When everyone was finally asleep,
Odysseus and his men leapt out.

They opened the city gates and all
the Greek soldiers charged into Troy.

The Trojans were shocked. They fought bravely but they could not stop Odysseus and the Greek army from destroying the whole of Troy.

Nothing was left of the city. People even forgot where it had stood.

But no one will ever forget the story of the great wooden horse.

Hopscotch has been specially designed to fit the requirements of the Literacy Framework. It offers real books by top authors and illustrators for children developing their reading skills. There are 63 Hopscotch stories to choose from:

* hardback